Ordering Information: www.TheKidonomicsSeries.com

Printed in Canada

About the Book

This book is the first in The Kidonomics Series promoting financial literacy for children. Wants and desires are unlimited but the resources necessary to fulfill these wants and desires, be it time or money, at some point are limited. Hence choices have to be made.

The ability to make the distinction between wants and needs and make a choice, is imperative in laying the foundation for being financially responsible.

The following books in the series go on to teach children about saving and spending. The triad of making choices, saving and spending wisely are crucial in developing financial awareness and financial acumen for children.

About the Author

Dr. M holds a PhD in Economics and has spent over a decade teaching Economics and Finance. She also has a Diploma in Early Childhood Education. In addition to lecturing at University of Toronto and being a full time financial consultant, Dr. M keeps busy with her two daughters. They were the inspiration for The Kidonomics Series which teaches children the fundamental economic skills for establishing a strong financial base.

Sara and Scott always loved shopping with Mom.
They loved going to the supermarket.

Today Mom needs to buy vegetables.
"Can I ride inside the cart?" asked Scott.
"You're a big boy now Scott,
I think you are too tall for the cart," said Mom with a smile.

SALE!
fizzy cola
Sprizzy

The kids always imagined that the supermarket was another world, a place to explore and find new things.

Today Mom needs to get cucumbers, tomatoes, and lettuce.

She also needs to pick up some cereal for breakfast. "You kids can decide on which box of cereal to get. You can each choose one box," said Mom.

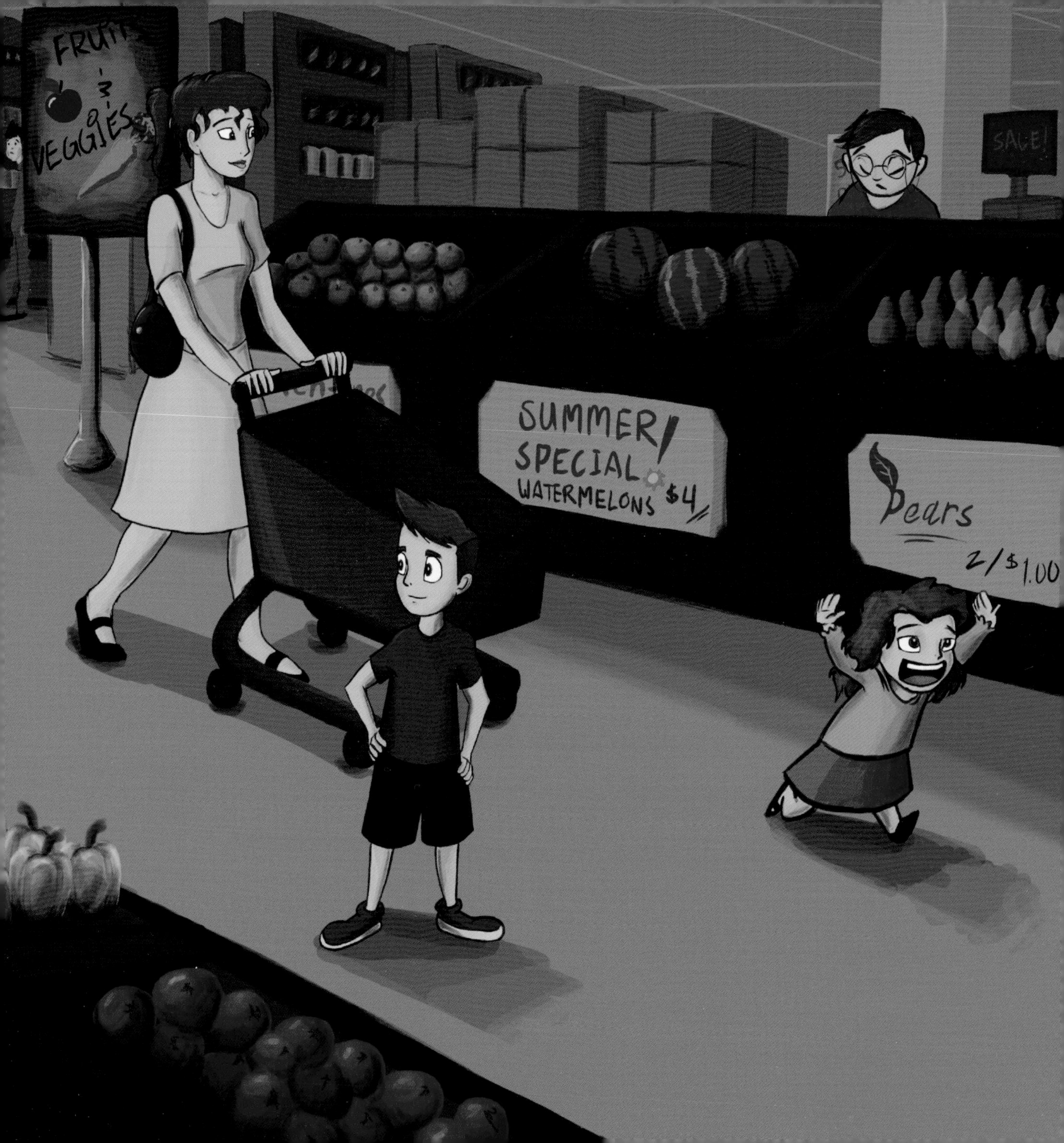

VEGGIES
SALE!
SUMMER SPECIAL! WATERMELONS $4
Pears 2/$1.00

Before the children got their cereal they followed Mom to the vegetable stall.

They watched her closely as she picked up the vegetables, examined them, and then put them back. This went on for a little while.

FRUITS
&
VEGGIES
SALE!
50% OFF!
Clementines
3/$1.00
Pears
2/$1.00

"Mom, what are you doing?" asked Scott.

"I am choosing the best vegetables, dear," said Mom.

"This tomato has a bruise, so I am looking for one that is nice and firm," Mom explained as she held up a tomato. "There are many vegetables here. I need only a few, so I choose carefully to make sure I get the freshest ones. That way my salad would be extra delicious!" continued Mom.

"Oh, I see, so you choose the best ones," exclaimed Scott.

"That's right! I am choosing the ones that we will all enjoy the most," replied Mom.

FRUITS
&
VEGGIES
Clementines
3/ $1.00
SUMMER
SPECIAL
WATERMELON
Pears
2/ $1.00
50% OFF!
SALE!

Now it was the children's turn to choose their cereal.
It was a big job!

When they got to the cereal isle, the children stood together and watched all the different types of cereal.

"There are so many. How can we decide?" asked Sara.

"You can do it. Just have a look and get the one that you think you will enjoy the most," replied Mom.

CORN CRISP
INVADER FLAKES
CRUNCHY-O
BEAR'S BREAKFAST
BOLTS
CEREAL GOODNESS
TRICKY FLAKES!
CLOUD-O's
FLAMING POPPERS
O-NATURAL CEREAL
GHOST-O CEREAL
ARCTIC FLAKES
HONEY-O's
SUNNY CRISP
KRUNCHY FLAKES

Sara picked up the pink box with the princess on it, the purple one with the ponies and the blue one with the fairies.

"I want them all" exclaimed Sara.
Mom told her she had to choose one.

"Choose one? Why can't I have all three?" Sara whined.
" Sara, you want three boxes but you only need one," explained Mom.

"No, I need all three," protested Sara.

" Sara do you know the difference between wanting something and needing something?" asked Mom.

Sara thought for a moment, "No," she said softly.

GHOST-O
EREAL

"A need is something you really have to have.
For example you really need to get a box of cereal for breakfast. If you don't, then you will not have any cereal to eat in the morning. So it is a need.

A want is something that you would like to have but if you didn't get it, it would be okay. You can still have cereal for breakfast even if you didn't get two extra boxes," explained Mom.

FLAKES
BOLTS

"Oh! So I need only one box but I want all three," said Sara.
"Yes. That's right. You need to choose one. Do you understand?" asked Mom with a smile.

Sara took a moment before she replied, "Yes Mom, I understand." Even though Sara understood that she had to choose, she found it very hard to decide.

Then she remembered her favorite story "Ribbit- Skibbit and the Pink Lettuce". In that story the little bunny, Skibbit also had to make a choice. Sara thought if Skibbit could make a choice so could she.

CHAMP'S
CEREAL
ARCTIC
FLAKES
$3.25
$3.55

Now, she had to be sure she chose the best box. The box that she would enjoy the most .

"I can do it Mom, I can make a choice!" said Sara proudly. "Let's see, I love princesses, ponies and fairies. Even though I love them all, I think I will take the Pony cereal because they have pink, purple and blue in them." reasoned Sara.

"Good choice Sara, well done! When this box is finished you can come back and get the Princess or the Fairy cereal." Mom explained.

"Yeah! That's great Mom! I am very happy about my choice. I can't wait for breakfast!" said Sara happily.

CHAMP'S CEREAL!
ARCTIC FLAKES

"What about you Scott, have you decided?" asked Mom.

"Yes I have. I love pirates, so I am taking
the Pirate cereal," said Scott proudly.

CLOUD-O's
MARSHMALLOW
FLAKES

BOLTS
FLAKES!

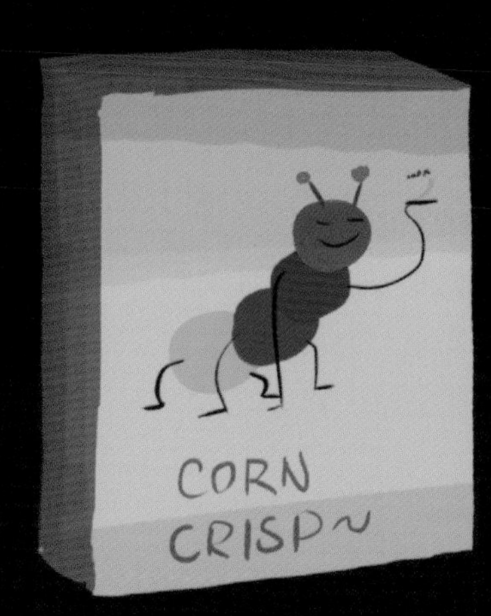
CORN
CRISP~

YELLOW
CRISP~

YAR
HAR!
PIRATE
CRUNCH!
KRUNCHY
FLAKES

"What about the Space cereal don't you love the stars too?" asked Mom.

Mom was curious to see whether Scott would change his mind.

"Yes I do, but I decided I want to get the Pirate cereal today. Maybe next time I can try the Space cereal," explained Scott.

"Great job Scott, excellent choice!" said Mom.
She was happy that Scott was able to choose so wisely.

FLAKES
BOLTS
CEREAL GOODNESS
TRICKY FLAKES!
YELLOW CRISP~
PETAL-O's
YAR HAR!
PIRATE CRUNCH!

"You kids did a great job today!

Let's ring these up and go home!" said Mom proudly.

HAVE A NICE DAY!
$14.99
Hearty soup
Soup~

The End